FIRE ON THE MOUNTAIN

By
Henry Bamman
Robert Whitehead

Illustrations
William Lackey

BENEFIC PRESS • **CHICAGO**
Publishing Division of Beckley-Cardy Company
Atlanta   Dallas   Long Beach   Portland

WHY? WHAT? WHERE?

To keep a forest fire in the Rocky Mountains from spreading, Mark and Rich parachute into the path of the fire. They rescue a camper who is hurt before the fire is at last put out.

WORLD OF ADVENTURE SERIES

The Lost Uranium Mine

Flight to the South Pole

Hunting Grizzly Bears

Fire on the Mountain

City Beneath the Sea

The Search for Piranha

Sacred Well of Sacrifice

Viking Treasure

Library of Congress
Number 63-21331

Copyright 1963 by Benefic Press
All Rights Reserved
Printed in the United States of America

Contents

The Smoke Jumpers

"There's a smoke!" Mark said. He pointed to a thin line of blue smoke that curled slowly into the sky from the top of the mountain off to the left.

Mark handed the field glasses to the young man at his side. Then he turned to the pilot. "Throw it on, Frank," he said. "Let's see how fast this thing will go."

The sound of the motor became much louder as the airplane picked up speed. Under the pilot's sure hand, the airplane came around slowly and headed right for the line of smoke that rose from the far mountain. Through the field glasses, Rich watched the smoke as it climbed up into the blue sky.

Mark and Rich were smoke jumpers. When a fire was seen in the mountains, it was their job to fly to the spot. When they reached the fire area, the two smoke jumpers parachuted down to the forest floor. That way they could reach a fire quickly and put it out before it burned too large an area of the forest.

The men watched the smoke closely with their field glasses. Soon they no longer had to use the glasses to see it. They could see the fire licking through the top branches of the trees, throwing flames high into the sky.

Suddenly, a voice came over the airplane's radio. "Green Wind. This is Blue Tower. Green Wind. This is Blue Tower. Can you hear me? Over."

"Green Wind! That's our call," said Mark. "Better get it, Rich."

"It must be that watch tower over there calling us," said Frank. He pointed down to a watch tower standing on a tall mountain off to the right.

Rich turned up the radio. Then he said into it, "Blue Tower. This is Green Wind. We hear you, Blue Tower. Over."

"Green Wind. This is Blue Tower," came the radio voice. "We see you now. How bad is the fire? Over."

"Blue Tower. This is Green Wind," said Rich. "We are almost over it. From the looks of the flames, you will have to radio the trucks and tell the men to move up fast. They don't have much time. It looks like a bad one this time. Over."

"Green Wind. This is Blue Tower," the voice said. "Got it. Will radio Red Trees. Move trucks up fast. Over and out."

"Right, Blue Tower," said Rich. "This is Green Wind. Over and out."

Rich reached over and turned down the radio. "Red Trees. Is that the radio call for our men coming up the mountain road to the fire?" asked Frank.

"Right," said Mark. "And they should get a move on from the looks of things down there."

The airplane was flying right over the fire now. Mark pointed down and called out to the pilot, "Take it down, Frank! Let's see if we can find an open spot in which to jump."

"All right, men," said Frank above the roar of the motor. "Here we go! Down!"

Suddenly the airplane nosed over and headed down toward the smoke and fire. Mark fell back, hitting his head against the side of the airplane. His hat fell down over his eyes. "Are you all right, Mark?" Rich asked him.

"I think so," said Mark, taking off his hat and brushing the top of his head with his hand. "But it's a good thing I had on this hard hat. This hat is what saved me."

"It's not the hard hat that saved you, though," laughed Rich. "It's your hard head!" Mark looked at Rich. Then he laughed about it, too.

As the airplane dropped lower and lower, the men could see that the top of the mountain was a tower of fire. Flames jumped from tree to tree, helped along by the wind. Here and there, red, hot flames licked through open fields, burning the grass. The smoke from the fire worked its way through the open door of the airplane.

As Mark looked down, he could not help but think about the forest. He had worked a long time in the Rockies. He knew all the trees and trails well. It was almost as if they were his. "And here they are, going up in smoke!" he thought.

He thought about the animals, too, the deer and the beaver. Would this fire storm kill them? Would some of them get away in time? "We must stop this fire!" he said to himself.

Suddenly, Rich spotted an open field. "There's a spot, Frank. See that green field!"

"I see it!" the pilot called out above the roar of the motor and the fire. He pulled the airplane up and turned it to the right. "I'm going to come around again and fly over that spot," he said. "Get ready to jump, men!"

"It's not a very big field, but it will have to do," said Mark. "It's right in the path of the fire, but I don't see a better place."

Mark and Rich looked over their packs and their parachutes. Then they worked their way slowly toward the open door of the airplane.

"Ready to go, Rich?" Mark asked, turning to the smoke jumper beside him.

"If you are ready, I'm ready," Rich called into his friend's ear. "You first."

Mark laughed. "You would, Rich!" he said. "I'll be surprised when the time comes that you do jump first. Get ready!"

Just then Frank called out to them, "Mark! Rich! That field is coming up fast. When I say 'go'. . ."

Mark pulled again at the straps that were holding his parachute and walkie-talkie radio in place. They were all right. Then he took his place at the open door of the airplane. He could feel Rich move up close behind him.

Mark looked down into the smoke. It was already making his eyes watery and red. He saw that the tops of the trees were much closer now. He was a little afraid. "It will not take long for me to get down to the ground from here, and it will take time for the parachute to open," Mark said to himself.

"Go, Mark!" came Frank's call to them.

Mark jumped. As he fell from the airplane, a hot wind brushed his face.

Quickly, Mark pulled the line to open his parachute as he turned over in the air. Sparks from the fire rose to pick at his eyes and hands. He could see the trees coming up closer. . .and closer. . .

"Falling fast. . .falling fast!" he thought. Still the parachute had not opened! "That 'chute better. . .!" he thought. "But then, why think about it? There is nothing I can do now if it doesn't open."

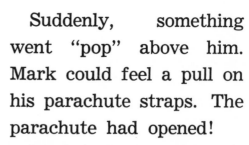

Suddenly, something went "pop" above him. Mark could feel a pull on his parachute straps. The parachute had opened!

Mark looked up through the smoke around him. Over his head, in the blue sky, he could see another parachute opening up. It was Rich. The airplane was moving away.

Then Mark crashed into something hard. He saw red. "Fire. . .burning. . .!" he thought. Suddenly, he found himself falling. . . falling. . .falling. (1191)

14

Caught In A Fire Storm

"Mark! Mark!"

Mark heard the voice calling, but he could not get his eyes to work together. His head hurt him terribly.

As he turned his head slowly toward the voice, his eyes began to clear. He could just see a face bending over him in the curling smoke. Then two big hands reached down to help him—Rich.

The air was hot and cutting, and Mark choked on it. Then Rich was throwing water into his face. "What. . .?" Mark began, turning his head away.

"You hit your head on something when you came down," said Rich, pointing to the tree above them. "It knocked you out, but good."

"Man, I'll say something did!" Mark said, running his hand over a cut above his left eye. "But how did I get here?"

"The wind caught your 'chute," Rich said. "You fell right into the middle of those trees. Mark, we have to get out of here fast. Look!"

Mark didn't have to look. He could feel, and the heat was terrible. He looked up into the smoky air over his head. He could see the flaming trees as they bent in the wind. The noise they made as they popped open from the heat was like bombs falling all about them. "This is a crown fire. The flames are in the tops of the trees," said Mark.

As Mark tried to get up, his heavy pack caught on a branch and almost pulled him down again. Rich caught him just in time. "Are you all right?" Rich asked him.

"I think so," said Mark as he stood up and pulled his pack into place.

Mark and Rich had parachuted into forest fires in the Rocky Mountains before. Mark was a young man with clear blue eyes and a friendly laugh. He knew the forest and his job well.

Rich was younger than Mark, but a little taller. The forest fighters called him the "Big One" because he had big hands and was a very big eater.

The fire roared on while the two men stood side by side in the forest, looking for a break in the smoke. The wind carried smoke into their already red eyes. Flaming branches fell down toward them from the tops of the burning trees.

Suddenly Mark called out, "Clear Stream!"

"What?" asked Rich, brushing smoke from his eyes.

"On the other side of this mountain! Clear Stream!" Mark called. "If we can get there. . ."

"But how?" Rich choked. "We are caught in here. By now the flames are sure to have reached around to the other side of the mountain."

"We will be killed if we wait here, though!" Mark called back above the roar of the flames. "The wind is against us."

"Mark is right," thought Rich. "The wind is against us and picking up all the time." Just then, the wind came roaring in over the trees, under the branches, and through the tall grass. Towers of flame ran before it, throwing down sparks right and left. All the while, the smoke became heavier and heavier.

"This is a fire storm for sure!" Rich called.

The wind and flame roared down on them again and again, licking through the trees around them. Curls of flaming brush went blowing by, giving off hissing sparks in the heat.

Suddenly Mark pointed off through the trees. "Rich. . .to the right. . . over there," he called out. "I don't think it's as bad. If we can find a break in the fire over there. . ."

Mark didn't have to say more. Rich had already moved up behind him. Walking fast, almost running, they started off through the trees. Flaming branches dropped down about them as they worked their way along under the burning trees.

Sparks fell on them, and
they had to stop now and
then to look over each
other's pack. All the while,
the packs became heavier and heavier. Mark had to
carry the walkie-talkie, as well as his shovel, pick and
axe. But the men knew they could not stop.

Suddenly, the men saw an opening in the tower of
flames before them. It was not much, just a little
opening. It seemed to be a rocky path running around
the side of the mountain.

"Rich, come on! This way!" Mark called out.

The two men walked much faster now, for the flames were already licking at the trees along the side of the path. Mark hoped that the flames had not yet reached all the way around the mountain. Their only hope was to get across the stream before the fire reached it.

Just then, through the trees, something caught Mark's eye—water! It was Clear Stream! But the fire had almost reached the stream!

"We have to make it," Mark said to himself. He turned to call Rich just in time to see Rich fall! Mark ran back up the trail quickly, reaching his friend's side just as the smoke jumper got up. Then Mark saw why Rich had fallen.

A large deer had been killed near the trail by the smoke, and Rich had fallen over it when he moved off the path. The two men stood and looked down at the deer. But there was nothing they could do for the animal now.

"We can't help the deer now!" Mark called into Rich's ear. "Clear Stream. . .almost there. . .come on, let's go!"

The two men ran on down the path toward the stream. Nearing the water, they saw that the flames were racing along downstream toward them.

"Quick, Rich, take off your pack and hold it above your head!" Mark called.

"That water looks deep," Rich said.

"But it's not that deep!" said Mark.

Working quickly, and holding their packs over their heads, the two men walked into the stream. No sooner had they reached the middle of it, than they heard a popping sound behind them. They stopped and turned. A large tree towered far above them. Its branches were covered with flames. Suddenly it began to bend in the wind.

"Rich, get out of the way!" Mark called out to the smoke jumper.

Then the flaming tree was falling down, headed right toward them! (1040)

The Plan

The falling tree crashed into the stream with a roar. The air was filled with a sudden hiss of steam as the flaming branches hit the water. The falling tree just missed the two men, throwing clouds of hot, steamy water over them.

"Man, that was close!" said Rich.

"You said it," said Mark. "Let's get going before another one falls and hits us."

Moving fast, the two men quickly reached the far side of the stream. There they fell to the ground, dropping their packs in the long grass. Far above them they could hear the loud noise of an airplane, even over the roar of the flames. But they could not see it through the smoke.

The men looked back across the stream through the heavy smoke. As far as the eye could see, trees were covered with flames. By this time, the fire had burned over much of the mountain.

"Where are we, Mark?" Rich asked.

"The north side of Clear Stream," Mark said. "That's Rose Mountain behind us."

The men could see that the fire was not going to stop at the stream. The fire had already jumped the stream at some points, and little spot fires flamed in the tall grass along their side of the stream. In places, it had started to move away from the stream and back toward the trees. Mark could see over those trees to the top of the mountain behind them. Suddenly, he knew what they had to do.

"Rich, give me a hand with this walkie-talkie, will you?" he asked. "We have things to do. I have a plan that I hope will work."

As he helped Mark take the radio from his back, Rich looked up the stream at the dark red flames moving slowly toward them through the grass. "From the looks of that fire we had better 'walkie' now and 'talkie' some other time," he said.

Mark just looked at his friend and laughed. Then he began to take the radio out. He looked it over very quickly and then turned it on.

"What's your plan, Mark?" Rich asked, watching the fire closely.

"First, I'm going to call Frank up there in the airplane," Mark said. "We must have chemical bombs dropped down here to help us stop this fire. Frank can do a better job of reaching the bomber pilot on his radio than we can."

Rich looked up toward the smoky sky. He could hear Frank's airplane up there, but he could not see it.

Suddenly, a voice came over the radio. "Red Hat! Red Hat! This is Green Wind. Do you hear me? Come in! Come in! Over!"

Mark picked up the radio and talked into it. "Green Wind. This is Red Hat. This is Mark, Frank. We hear you. Over."

"Red Hat. This is Green Wind," came back Frank's voice. "Mark, where have you and Rich been? I have been calling and calling you. Over."

"Green Wind. This is Red Hat. We dropped right into the middle of the fire and had a hard time getting out. Over."

"I thought you two had had it," said Frank's voice again. "Where are you now? Over."

"We are on the north side of Clear Stream," said Mark. "Can you see the stream from where you are, Frank? Over."

"No. There's too much smoke. Flames have now covered all of the mountain. I can just make out the water trucks coming up the road behind Rose Mountain, the road north of where you must be. Over."

Mark talked into the radio again. "Frank, this is a bad one—a crown fire—and it's running fast. It has already killed some animals. We found a deer just off the trail. But I think we can stop the fire with your help. Over."

"Red Hat. This is Green Wind. I'm all ears. What is the plan? Over."

"All right, Frank. Now get this," said Mark. "The fire has already jumped the stream and started more fires than Rich and I can put out. Call the bomber in. Have the pilot drop his chemicals on this side of Rose Mountain, near the middle. There is a tall stand of grass there that runs clear across the mountain. He can't miss seeing it. By the time he gets there, the fire will have reached that spot. Have you got that, Frank? Over."

"All right, Mark," Frank's voice came in again. "I understand. Over."

"Another thing," Mark said. "Rich and I will move around the mountain and help the men put up a fire line on the back side of the mountain near the top. With the chemicals and the fire line, I think we can stop the fire. Over."

"Red Hat. This is Green Wind," said Frank over the radio. "Plan sounds good. I'll call in bomber to make his run and drop his chemicals along the grass line in the middle of Rose Mountain. You will fall back and help the men hold a line on the back side of the mountain. Right? Over."

"Green Wind. This is Red Hat. Right, Frank. Over and out."

"Red Hat. This is Green Wind," came Frank's voice again. "Blue Tower tells me there is a camper some place near you down there. Keep an eye open for him. Over and out."

"Green Wind. This is Red Hat. We will watch for camper. Over and out."

Mark turned off the walkie-talkie, picked it up, and began strapping it on his back again. Then he reached down to pick up his pack.

"Did you get all of that, Rich?" he asked.

"I think so," said Rich, "but. . ." Then he stopped, for suddenly the two men heard something like the call of an animal. It seemed to be coming from far down the stream.

"What was that?" Mark asked.

"I don't know," Rich said.

The two men turned and faced downstream. They listened closely. There! There it was again!

"Why, that sounds like a man's voice!" Mark said.

Suddenly, each man knew. "The camper!" the two men said together.

"Let's go!" Mark called.

But Rich was already running downstream. He dropped his pack behind him. Mark dropped his pack, too, and ran down the stream after Rich.   (1046)

A Race Against Time

As the two men ran along the side of the stream, the sound of the voice calling out became harder and harder to hear. "What do you think is going on, Mark?" asked Rich as they ran on.

"I don't know," Mark said. "It sounds as if the man is hurt. And if he's on the other side of this stream. . ." Here Mark let his voice trail away, for suddenly, the call for help came again. The call was nearer now, just across the stream from them.

The men stopped and listened, trying to pick up the sound above the roar of the fire. But they heard nothing, and the smoke was too heavy for them to see very far into the trees.

"We will just have to go across here, Rich," Mark said. "But it will have to be quick. We don't have much time before those flames will be down on top of us."

"Let's go then," Rich called. With that, he jumped into the stream and began making his way through the water with Mark close behind.

Suddenly, the camper's call came again, much clearer now, "Help! Help me!"

"Hold on! We are coming!" Rich called out above the noise of the flames.

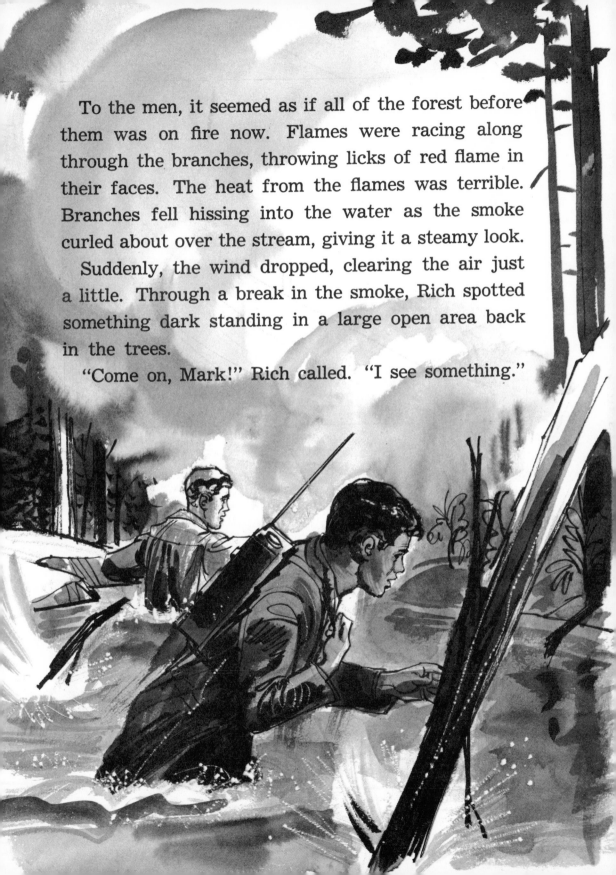

To the men, it seemed as if all of the forest before them was on fire now. Flames were racing along through the branches, throwing licks of red flame in their faces. The heat from the flames was terrible. Branches fell hissing into the water as the smoke curled about over the stream, giving it a steamy look.

Suddenly, the wind dropped, clearing the air just a little. Through a break in the smoke, Rich spotted something dark standing in a large open area back in the trees.

"Come on, Mark!" Rich called. "I see something."

Quickly, the two men reached the brush lining the stream. They climbed up out of the water and running low, to keep from getting hit by bent branches, soon reached the clearing. To their surprise, they saw a large tent standing before them. One side of the tent had been knocked down by a large branch that still lay across it.

"He must be in there!" Mark called into Rich's ear.

The two men ran to the tent, and reaching it, pulled off the cover over an opening at the back. Looking in, they saw a man on the ground. His eyes were closed and he was very still.

The man opened his eyes and turned toward them slowly. He tried to sit up. "Help me! Save me!" he said in a heavy voice. Then he fell back.

Mark and Rich dropped to the man's side. They could see that he was badly hurt. His thin face was very red, and there was a long, deep cut on the side of his head.

"Are you hurt any other place?" asked Mark as he looked at the man's head.

"My left leg," the man said. "Something fell on the tent and hit me on the side of the head. I was knocked out for a while."

"There's a big branch across the tent out there," Rich said, looking down at the man.

"Well, when I came to, my head hurt something terrible," the man went on. "I tried to stand up, but my leg just would not hold me.

"Then the fire started. I could hear it coming through the trees. I knew I was going to be killed when the flames reached me."

The man stopped and looked up at the two men. "Who are you?" he asked.

"Smoke jumpers," Rich said. "We parachuted in here to fight the fire. We heard your call."

"That's a break for me!" the man said.

"Can you walk now?" Mark asked, running his hand over the man's left leg.

"No, I can't," said the man. "My leg. . ." He covered his face with his hands.

"Well, we will have to carry you out, then," said Rich. "First, though, let's see what we can do about that leg of yours."

Working rapidly, Mark and Rich found some green branches that were not yet burned. They placed these on the man's bad leg, using the straps cut from the tent opening to hold them in place. Then they cut away some of the tent covering to put over their heads to keep out the heat.

"Now, my friend," said Mark, reaching down, "let's see if you can stand."

34

"Just call me Pete," the
man said.

Pete tried to stand on
one leg with Mark's help,
but he almost fell. Mark caught him just in time.

"All right, Pete, just take it slow," Mark said.

Mark and Rich made a chair with their hands and
carried Pete from the tent. Above the tent, a large
tree bent in the wind as the fire raced through its
top branches.

"Which way?" Rich asked. "Toward the stream?"

"We can't make it back that way," Mark said. "Take
a good look."

Turning, Rich saw that the fire had already raced on down the side of the stream. The brush along the side of the stream was burning. There was no way to reach the water. They were cut off.

"The only thing we can do is move on downstream with the fire and hope that we can find a way across the stream," said Mark.

"Let's get going then!" Rich said.

Pete was heavy, but Mark and Rich moved along very fast. At times, it was hard to see through the smoke that was blowing all about them.

Suddenly Mark said, "Hold it, Rich!'

The two men stopped and put Pete down on the ground. Then they turned and looked back. Through the curls of smoke, they could see the flames racing along on all sides, climbing rapidly through the trees and brush. The fire was closing in on them fast. There was no turning back now!

The only thing the men could see before them was the face of a mountain. The trees and brush at the top of the mountain were already on fire. Burning branches dropped down its side, crashing to the forest floor near them.

The men were caught. On one side was a mountain; on the other, a flaming forest. There was no way out for them! (1059)

36

In the Mine

Suddenly, Mark thought of something. A long time back, while clearing out trees in this area, he had seen an old mine. At the time, he had only looked in it. If they could find that mine again. . .

"We are not licked yet," he called to Pete. Then turning to Rich he said, "We have to find cover fast. There used to be an old mine around here. Let's see if we can find it."

"Which way?" Rich asked him.

"Over there," Mark said, pointing toward the heavy brush at the foot of the mountain. "Come on!"

The two men picked Pete up and carried him through the grass. Reaching the rocks at the foot of the mountain, the two smoke jumpers lowered the camper to the ground.

"That old mine is right around here some place," Mark said, looking around through the smoke. "I'll look up this way, Rich. You look around down there."

The area was heavily covered with tall grass, some of it already burning in spots. The ground was very rocky. In the smoke, it was hard to find the mine opening. But Rich, moving about through the rocks to his left, suddenly called out, "Here it is, Mark."

Mark ran to Rich's side. There, in the side of the mountain, he saw a dark opening. Tall grass nearly covered the opening, and Rich had almost missed it. It was not a very big opening, but the men knew that they could get through it.

"Come on, let's get Pete," Rich said.

The two men raced back to where they had left the camper and very quickly carried him to the mine. Mark went in first. Then he and Rich helped Pete through the opening.

The mine was very dark, but the men could see that it was not deep and had not been worked much. They could stand up in it. On the floor was some old wood that had been cut and used to hold up the sides of the mine. Here and there drops of water streamed down the sides of the mine and stood in low spots on the rocky floor.

"How's he doing?" Mark asked as they put Pete down on the floor of the mine.

"Not so good," said Rich. "This smoke and heat. . . well, it will kill all of us."

The sound of the flames burning the forest already came to their ears. Smoke began to make its way into the mine. The fire was coming closer.

"Don't give up yet, Rich!" Mark said. "We can make it if we keep our heads."

"But what can we do?" Rich asked.

"Well, first, let's see if the two of us can close up that opening," Mark said.

Working fast, the two men took some of the wood and stood it against the opening into the mine. In no time, they had it closed off. But smoke still curled through openings in the wood.

Mark took some of the covering they had used on their heads and put it over the wood. Then using his hat to pick up some of the water on the ground, he began throwing water on the covering and on the wood. He was trying to water the wood down in hopes of holding back the smoke.

Then the men waited. Above the sound of the flames, they could hear the hiss of burning brush as the fire came closer and closer to the mine. The thin cover of smoke in the mine became heavier, climbing in clouds about them.

Mark lay down on the floor. "Rich! Down on the floor!" Mark choked out. "The air is a little better down here!"

For a long time, a very long time, the men lay face down on the floor of the mine with the choking smoke cutting into them. The heat was terrible, almost too much to stand, even though the men filled their hats with water and let it run down over their heads.

Then slowly, very slowly, the sound of the roaring flames began to fall away. The men could no longer hear the popping of trees and branches. The smoke in the mine thinned out.

After waiting some time, Mark got up and made his way to the mine opening. Pulling off the covering and knocking down the hot wood, he looked out. What lay before him in the clearing was terrible to see. There was not a spot of grass that was not burned. Clouds of smoke from the burned trees climbed up toward the sky. All around, trees hissed from the heat.

As Mark stood there, looking out over the clearing, Rich came up and stood by his side. "How's Pete?" Mark asked him.

"He's not too good, but I think he will make it," Rich said.

"Are you all right?" Mark asked.

"I think so," said Rich, looking out over the burned, smoky forest. "Not much left, is there."

"Only one thing," said Mark.

"What's that?" asked Rich.

"Us!" Mark said.   (843)

Up the Mountain

As Mark and Rich walked together from the mine, they found that the fire was far from over. The wind was still blowing hard, and flaming branches were dropping down from the mountain top above. The heat was terrible. There was nothing they could do but go back into the mine and wait it out.

"There are two bad things about this," said Rich. "One is that we can't help out up on the mountain."

"What's the other thing?" Mark asked.

"I still have had nothing to eat," Rich said.

"Things are bad," Mark laughed.

When the two men turned back into the mine, they found Pete feeling better. But he still could not stand or walk by himself. "You two have been good to me," he said. "I would have been killed if. . ."

"Don't talk now, Pete," Rich said. "We have a long way to go yet."

After a while, the heat seemed to have reached a low point. When the men left the mine again, they found the air clearer and not as cutting. Carrying Pete, Mark and Rich worked their way through the burned forest toward the stream. Now and then they had to take the long way around some tree or bushy area that flamed up suddenly in their path.

The men stopped when they reached the stream. They could hear the sound of flames from far-off Rose Mountain. But they could not see the mountain. It was covered by clouds of smoke.

"What do you think is going on up there?" Rich asked Mark.

"It's hard to tell with all this smoke," Mark said. "I don't hear the airplanes. But from the heaviness of the air, I would say that the bomber has dropped its chemicals. That's what's making all the smoke."

"I'm not too sure," said Rich. "From the sound of it, that fire is still burning very fast in the tops of the trees. It can't be out yet."

"Well, just talking about it will not help," Mark said. "We should work our way downstream. The fire seems to have burned out down there. There's not too much smoke."

"The fire road running up behind Rose Mountain cuts down to the stream some place down there, too," Rich said.

"Right," said Mark. "Come on. Let's get moving."

Working their way along the stream, the men made good time. It was not long before they reached the point where the fire had burned out. The flames had been stopped by the rocky face of a mountain that came down to the stream.

Just across the stream, the men could see the fire road as it branched away from the creek and rose on up behind the mountain. But nothing could be seen on the road—no trucks and no men!

"Well, we will just have to walk it," Rich said after they had moved across the stream. They were still carrying Pete.

"Why not put me down here and come back after me?" Pete asked.

"No, we will all go together," Mark said. "We. . ."

But just then the sound of a truck motor came to their ears. Through the smoke, a red truck came nosing down the fire road. When the men in the truck saw who it was, they jumped out and came running toward the smoke jumpers.

"Mark! Rich!" said one of the men. "Where have you two been?"

"We were sure you had been killed," said another.

"Here, help us with this man," said Mark. "He's been hurt."

Two of the men carried Pete to the truck and put him on the floor in the back. Then these two men got into the back of the truck with him while Mark and Rich climbed in with the driver. The motor roared, and the truck turned around and started back up the road toward the fire.

"How are things going up on the fire line, Mike?" Mark asked, turning to the driver.

"Some good, some bad," said Mike. "We seem to have it licked along the sides. But on the mountain— that's another thing.

"The bomber made a good drop and it slowed the fire down," he went on. "But when the pilot had to go back and get more chemicals, the fire picked up again. I don't know if we can hold it back now."

"Who is the head man?" Mark asked.

"Kip Black," said the driver. "But you are to take over when you get there, Mark."

"Let me have that radio, Mike," said Mark. "I would like to talk to Frank, our fire spotter, up there in the airplane.

"Green Wind. Green Wind. This is Red Hat," said Mark, turning up the radio. "Come in, Green Wind. Come in. Over."

"Red Hat. This is Green Wind," came Frank's voice. "Is that you, Mark? Come in. Over."

"Right, Frank," Mark called back. "What can you tell me about the fire? Over."

"Just what I have been telling Red Trees," said Frank. "The bomber is on its way back to you again. The pilot had the fire knocked down, but from here it looks as if it's running hard again. The fire has burned on through the grass, even though we had it well covered with chemicals. Over."

"Green Wind. This is Red Hat. Tell the pilot to get here as quickly as he can. And Frank, tell them to fly that helicopter in, will you? We could use it to carry men to spot fires that flame up back of our line. Over and out."

"Red Hat. This is Green Wind. Will do, Mark. Over and out."

Mark reached over and turned down the radio. Then he turned to the driver at his side. "Get a move on, Mike," he said. "We have a fire to go to."

"Right, Mark," said the driver.

The truck suddenly seemed to jump as it began to speed up the mountain road. (991)

Smoke Jumpers Under Fire

The road going up the mountain soon became nothing more than a cut through the trees. Branches brushed against the side of the truck as it made its way along very slowly. The smoke became much heavier.

Before them, the trail opened into a clearing. Through the trees, the men saw a large water truck.

"Our camp," Mike said.

As the truck ground to a stop, Mark and Rich jumped out, calling back to the men in the truck to look after Pete.

"Mark! Rich!" called out a tall man with a red face who was standing near the water truck. "It's good to see that you two are all right. We were afraid that something. . ."

"I'm all right, Kip, but Rich is not," said Mark.

"Where are you hurt, Rich?" asked Kip.

"Well. . ." laughed Rich, running his hand over his middle, "we could sure use a little something to keep us going."

"That again!" laughed Kip. He pointed to some men standing around a truck close by. "Try over there by that truck, Rich. But don't eat all of it."

"Now, what about the fire, Kip?" asked Mark after Rich had left. "Mike filled us in on some of it."

"Well, we have had our ups and downs, and I don't know if we can stop it or not," Kip said. "We have twenty men ready to move up to the fire line now. Each man has a pack with a water tank, axe, shovel, and pick."

"Any flame throwers?" asked Mark.

"We have two," said Kip.

Mark looked off toward the mountain. Then he turned back to the fire fighter. "Kip, here's my plan," he said. "On this side of the mountain, near the top, there's a stand of grass that runs all the way around the mountain. You take ten of the twenty men and two of the flame throwers and set up a line on the left in that grass. Rich and I will take the other ten men and set up a line on the right.

"Start some backfires with your flame throwers. With the wind blowing the way it is, those fires will burn toward the top of the mountain. When the crown fire coming up the other side hits your backfire at the top, they will burn each other out."

"Sounds good to me," Kip said.

"But, Kip, don't let your backfires get away," Mark said. "And keep looking for spot fires behind you. As soon as the helicopter gets here, we can have the pilot fly over the fire line. He can find and knock out those hot spots."

"Right!" said Kip.

Quickly, Mark and Kip got their men together to tell them the plan. In no time at all, two thin lines of fire fighters, carrying heavy packs, were working their way up the side of the mountain.

As the men climbed on through the forest, the wind picked up. The wind was carried along by the pull of the fire racing up the other side of the mountain. The air became very heavy with smoke.

After climbing for some time, Kip's men moved off to the left through a thin stand of trees. Mark and Rich and the other fire fighters went on. Soon they came out on a grassy field. The men stopped. Facing them across the open field was another stand of trees that rose high into the sky. Behind that lay the top of the mountain. It was crowned by clouds of dark, heavy smoke.

"We must be near the top," said Rich. "The smoke is getting much heavier."

"You are right," said Mark. "This is the clearing I was telling you about. We can set up a good fire line right here."

Mark then turned to the other men. "Now listen, men," he said. "Here's what we are going to do. Each of you is to find a spot running along a line through this field. Cover as much of the field as you can, but don't go so far that you can't still see one another. When all of you are in place, Rich and I will come along and start a backfire near you. Your job will be to hold the fire there and let the wind carry it up the side of the mountain."

Mark said, "When Rich and I reach the end of the line, we will come back and work as trailers. We will put out the the spot fires that get behind you."

"Do all of you understand that?" Rich asked.

"We understand!" the men said.

"All right, then. Let's go!" said Mark. "And, men, keep watching that wind."

Each of the fire fighters found a place for himself in the tall grass. Then working from the far right, Rich and Mark moved through the field, starting fires with the flame thrower. With a hiss, fire popped from the end of the flame thrower, spotting the grass with red licks of flame.

When Mark and Rich reached the far end of the line, they looked back. Even now, they could see those places where the spot fires had branched out and were racing up the mountain. Flames were already climbing into some of the low branches of the trees lining the clearing. Mark had picked his spots well.

"So far so good," said Mark.

"Come on, Mark," said Rich. "We had better start watching for spot fires behind the men."

They began just in time, too. Sparks were already jumping the fire line, starting spot fires behind the men. Mark and Rich stopped these spot fires very quickly, throwing streams of water on them from their pack water tanks.

Here and there along the line of fire, the flames began to curl back down the mountain. These spots had to be caught fast. Working with another man, Mark would knock down the flames with a handy branch from a tree. Then Rich would come along with his pick and shovel and clear away the brush from along the fire line.

Now and then a little tree behind the men would suddenly begin to smoke, having caught a spark in its branches. Then Rich's big axe came in handy as he very quickly cut down the tree. Mark would throw a stream of water on it to make sure the spark was out.

Rich was working side by side with Mark on one of these trees when he suddenly stopped and put up his hand. "Hold it, Mark!" he said. "Did you just hear something?"

The two men stood still and listened. They could hear the roar of the flames. But there was another sound, too. It was far off, from up on the mountain. The sound was carried to them by a sudden back pull of wind which dropped sparks all about them.

"What do you think it is?" Rich asked.

"It sounds as though an animal or man is up there near the top of the mountain," Mark said.

"But how could there be?" asked Rich. "There is no one who. . ." Then he stopped.

"Are you thinking what I'm thinking?" Mark asked. "Kip could have moved a man out as a feeler to find the end of our line. In this smoke, he could have missed us and moved too far up the mountain."

"Well, here we go again!" said Rich. He dropped his axe and ran toward the fire line, picking up his pack water tank as he ran.

Mark ran right behind him. He stopped only to strap on his pack, too. Then the two men raced on, looking for an opening in the burning grass.　(1282)

The Flames Are Out

Running along the fire line, Rich suddenly spotted a rocky path that the fire had not yet reached. "Mark! Over here!" he called. "There is an animal trail through here!"

"It looks like it!" said Mark as he ran up. "Come on! Let's try it!"

Running low along the path, the two men quickly found their way through the backfire. When they were through the burning brush and bent trees, they stopped to look back. The forest behind them was covered with red flames.

"This is terrible!" Rich called. "Mark, we can't. . ."

"There is no turning back now, Rich," Mark said. "Come on!"

Side by side, the two men went on, crashing through the brush. The smoke was very heavy in spots, and the men could hardly see their hands before their eyes. The air was so hot and steamy that water ran down their backs under their packs.

Suddenly, the smoke began to thin out, and the two men saw curls of blue in the sky over their heads. They knew they had reached the top of Rose Mountain.

The young men were very surprised to find that the wind, blowing up the mountain from all sides, had cleared the air at this point. From this high ground, they could look down the sides of the mountain. What they saw made them a little afraid.

Clouds of red flame that seemed to reach out for them raced up the mountain from all sides. On the far side of Clear Stream, the forest was topped with a climbing cover of roaring fire. The red, licking fire raced on, closer and closer.

Suddenly, from close by, a long, low sound reached their ears. "What was that?" Rich asked.

The men stood still and listened. Then the sound came again from some heavy brush near them.

Quickly, the men made their way toward the spot. Reaching down, they pulled back the brush slowly. From deep down in the brush, they saw two dark little eyes looking out at them.

"A beaver!" said Rich. "All this for a. . .!"

The animal let out a low, hissing sound and backed away. He was a little thing, but he was afraid and ready to fight.

Mark bent down and caught the beaver behind the ears. He picked him up.

"What have we here?" Rich asked, pulling on a strap curling around the beaver's back.

"I don't know for sure," Mark said. "But a while back we dropped some beavers in here by parachute from an airplane. This looks like a parachute strap to me, so he must be one of them. We were hoping the animals would eat the 'chute straps off."

"Come on!" said Rich, looking around him. "Let's get out of here!"

"We can't get through, Rich!" said Mark. "Take a good look!"

The flames towered above them, higher and higher, throwing sparks down into the clearing where they stood. The trees bent in the wind, their branches covered with flames from head to foot. The loud hiss of the flames; the wind that rose and dropped, curled and turned; the crashing of falling trees; all these sounds filled the air. There were no openings through the fire! The men were caught at the top of the mountain with fire all around them!

Suddenly, above the noise of the flames, Mark and Rich heard the sound of something over their heads. Then, through the thin cover of smoke, a helicopter dropped down out of the sky, throwing trails of smoke about in the clearing. The two men just stood and watched in surprise as the helicopter dropped lower and lower. The pilot nosed the helicopter along the top of the grass.

Mark and Rich knew the pilot was looking for them. They were soon racing across the field, calling out. The pilot must have seen them, for the helicopter suddenly headed right toward them.

65

When the helicopter reached them, it stopped still in the air, just above the ground. Hands reached down to pull them through the door. With the beaver still in his hand, Mark was pulled up through the opening. Rich came through right after him. Then the helicopter rose slowly into the air.

"Man, what a break for us that you men came along!" choked Mark, as he looked at the men standing around him, brushing him off.

"How did you find us?" Rich asked in a low voice.

"Your men radioed us that you had come up here," said one of the men. "We came in low, hoping to spot you. Suddenly, there you were!"

"Man, you were just in time!" said Rich.

"And so were you," said the pilot, pointing out of the helicopter. "Look!"

Mark and Rich looked down into the forest just in time to see the two fires that raced up the sides of the mountain crash into each other with a terrible roar. The helicopter was rocked as clouds of flames climbed high into the sky. Even where they were, the men could feel the heat given off by the flames.

Then from out of the sky to the north, a big bomber came racing in, dropping a cloud of chemicals over the spot. A crown of smoke rose suddenly into the air as the chemicals hit the ground. The head of the fire flamed low, and much of it went out. Behind the bomber, high in the sky, the two smoke jumpers saw another airplane—Frank!

As Mark stood there, looking down on the burned forest, something nosed against his hand. He looked down to see the beaver licking his hand. Just as Rich turned to say something, he saw Mark pick up the animal and hold it close.

"Well, little beaver, the fire is almost out now," Mark said. "Soon you and other animals can go back to the forest. Rich and I helped to save the forest for you. And we helped to save it for us, too." (1000)

8452

Vocabulary

The total vocabulary of this book is 347 words. Of these, 319 are below third grade and are not listed; 18 are third grade and appear in roman type; 10 are above third grade and appear below in italic type. The numbers indicate the page on which the word first appears.

already   11
area   5
axe   19

beaver   9
bombs   16

chemical   24
choked   15
crashed   12
crown   16

flames   5

helicopter   50
hissing   17

job   5

licking   5

motor   5

parachute   5
pilot   5

rapidly   34

shovel   19
sparks   13
speed   5
steam   23
straps   11

tanks   52
terrible   15
tower   6
trails   9

understand   27

* The number in parentheses on the last page of each chapter indicates the total number of words in that chapter. The number underlined on the last page of the story indicates the total number of words in the entire story.

Reading Maps

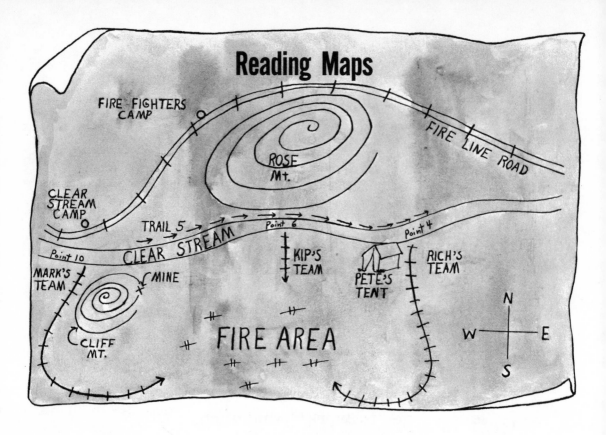

Mark and Rich were flying over the area south of Clear Stream where the fire had started to break out again. As the helicopter climbed above the smoke, Mark made a map of the fire area.

"What do you think about this fire, Mark?" Rich asked as he looked at the map.

"It doesn't look too bad right now," said Mark. "But it's going to be dark soon and some of the men have worked very hard already. Let's truck the men back down the Fire Line Road from the camp. We can set up another camp where the road runs close to Clear Stream. That's where we met Mike."

"I see," said Rich. "Then what?"

"We will set up three fire-fighting teams," said Mark. "I'll take one team and cross Clear Stream at Point 10 where we crossed with Pete. We will move south and west of Cliff Mountain and the mine and come up on the fire from the southwest."

"All right," said Rich. "I'll take another team along Trail 5 and cross the stream at Point 4, near where we found Pete's tent. We'll go around east of the fire and work our way up from the southeast."

"Right!" said Mark. "Then Kip can take a team along Trail 5 and cross Clear Stream at Point 6. He can move down toward the fire from the north."

"Then let's get to work!" said Rich.

News Story

NEW FIRE-FIGHTING PLAN USED AT CLEAR STREAM

DPI—The Clear Stream mountain area, long a friendly spot for campers and animals, has been hard hit by a forest fire. The fire has now been stopped by fire-fighting teams using the "cut-and-bomb" plan of fighting fires.

The "cut-and-bomb" plan uses men, machines, water, and chemicals. Fire fighters cut down the trees and grass around the fire that are not burned. Then they bomb the fire with chemicals and with water.

Trucks holding up to 1500 gallons of water move up close to the fire line. From there, the fire fighters carry the water in 5-gallon tanks strapped to their backs up to the "hot spots"—areas where the fire is the most hot. Streams of water from the tanks are then turned on these "hot spots."

In areas where trucks can not reach the fire, low-flying airplanes are used. To put out the fire, these planes drop chemicals from 50-gallon tanks.

The airplane flies low over the fire. Then the pilot opens the gate that holds the chemicals in their tanks. The chemicals fall out, covering the flames. Over 20,000 gallons of chemicals have been dropped on the Clear Stream fire.

Helicopters have been used to drop men into the forest fire area.

Men still make up the first line in fire fighting, but more and more machines are helping men do the work of fighting fires.

"Tall Tales"

Rose Mountain is not like other mountains. But now and then the fire fighters who work there tell stories which make the mountain seem even more strange than it really is. As you read this story, look for the things that make the story even "taller" than the mountain.

More than once, Rose Mountain has been hit by fire. One time a woodpecker started a fire on the mountain. The woodpecker pecked so hard and fast that sparks went flying into the air and came down again, starting a grass fire.

A mountaineer who had a stand of corn growing on the mountainside went out and found that the corn had popped in the field from the heat of a fire. Just then a beaver ran onto the field. The beaver thought the popped corn was snow, and froze to death right on the spot.

Things grow well on Rose Mountain, too. A man out for a walk saw a deer standing under a cherry tree. Suddenly one of the cherries fell on the deer. Before his very eyes, the man saw a cherry tree begin to grow out of the deer's head. Later the man killed the deer and had deermeat and cherry pie at the very same time.